Egg Poems

Compiled by John Foster

Contents

Acknowledgements

The Editor and Publisher wish to thank the following who have kindly given permission for the use of copyright material:

Jean Kenward for 'Ducks Feeding' © 1990 Jean Kenward; Brian Moses for 'Hatching Eggs' © 1990 Brian Moses; Judith Nicholls for 'Cuckoo'; 'Who can tell?' and 'Crack, Chip, Cheep,' all © 1990 Judith Nicholls; Irene Rawnsley for 'Egg Hatch' and 'Feeding the Ducks' both © 1990 Irene Rawnsley; Ian Serraillier for 'The Nest Egg' © 1990 Ian Serraillier.

Although every effort has been made to contact the owners of copyright material, a few have been impossible to trace, but if they contact the Publisher, correct acknowledgement will be made in future editions.

Egg Hatch

Tiptoe
to the incubator,
try not to speak.
Listen to the tap
of a little chick's beak.

Keep very still
when you come to watch;
there's a baby chick
beginning to hatch.

First a hole
then a crack
then a cheep cheep!
Soon he'll be exploring
on his big clawed feet.

Irene Rawnsley

cheep cheep!

He is just a fluffy chicken

He is just a fluffy chicken.
He is only one day old.
His beak is sort of yellow.
The rest of him is gold.
'Cheep, cheep,' is all he says.
It doesn't mean a lot.
But it's all that he can utter.
It's all the speech he's got.

Finola Akister

cheep cheep!

Hatching Eggs

Daniel wrote 'D' on his egg
and Carly pencilled a 'C'.
Trish drew a face on hers
but Martin just wrote 'Me'.

One was left for Emma
absent with chicken pox.
We placed it with the others
in the incubator box.

'How long will it take,' we asked,
'before our chicks are born?'
'Twenty-one days,' our teacher said,
'as long as we keep them warm.'

We listened everyday until
the chicks began to squeak.
Then cracks appeared in shells
and all at once a beak!

Our eyes were window-wide
as the little chicks broke free.
It wasn't everyday we saw
such magic in class 1B.

Brian Moses

Wishes

Said the first little chicken,
With a queer little squirm,
'I wish I could find
A fat little worm.'

Said the next little chicken,
With a sharp little squeal,
'I wish I could find
Some nice yellow meal.'

Said the third little chicken,
With a small sigh of grief,
'I wish I could find
A little green leaf.'

'See here,' said the mother,
From the green garden patch,
'If you want any breakfast,
Just come here and scratch.'

Anon

Cuckoo

Mother cuckoo lies in wait,
watching every nest.
Sparrow, pipit, robin —
which would be best?

Which nest shall I choose now,
for my eggs today?
Who will keep them warmest?
Where shall I lay?

Watches small hedge sparrows
busy fetching twigs.
These are workers, I can see,
they'll have my eggs!

Takes one egg from every nest,
throws it to the ground;
lays instead her cuckoo egg,
leaves with no sound.

These nests I have chosen
for my eggs today.
They will keep them warmest,
here shall I lay!

Judith Nicholls

David Holmes '89

Who can tell?

How big is a dinosaur egg?
Bigger than a tennis ball,
smaller than a tree?
Taller than a turtle shell
but not as tall as me?
Who can see?

How hard is a dinosaur egg?
Harder than a chicken's
but not as hard as steel?
Tough enough to make you think
it isn't really real?
Who can feel?

What might hatch from a dinosaur egg?
Diplodocus, stegosaurus
with its spiny tail?
Allosaurus, brontosaurus
tapping at the shell?
Who can tell?

Judith Nicholls

Crack, Chip, Cheep!

Down the path
behind the shed
inside our old wheelbarrow
is a heap of grass
and feathers and straw —
and six eggs from a sparrow!

One day Mum
said, 'Tiptoe down
then hold your breath and watch!
I think I heard
one tiny crack —
you might just see them hatch!'

We hurried down
without a word;
already in the straw
was a tiny snippet
of skin and bone,
the smallest I ever saw!

We stood and stared
as each shell cracked
and a bird wobbled into our barrow.
Could such a floppy
helpless thing
really turn into a sparrow?

Judith Nicholls

Ducks Feeding

Ducks at the water's edge
swimming for bread
eagerly hurrying,
keen to be fed:
rare ones and common ones,
coloured and white,
with feet that are paddles
and eyes that are bright.

Smart ones and shiny ones
preening a feather,
bustling and fidgeting,
greedy together:
pretty ones, perky ones,
pushing to come,
grabbing and swallowing. . ..

That's the last crumb!

Jean Kenward

Feeding the ducks

Flapping their wings
And scattering water drops,
The squabbling ducks
Gobble up bread.

John throws crusts.
Jane throws cake.
But hungry little Ted
Won't throw his biscuits –
He gobbles them instead.

Irene Rawnsley

The Nest Egg

There was once a greedy woman
who had a wonder hen.
It used to lay
a silver egg each day.
'Ho! Ho!' she thought. 'If I feed it
twice as much, it will lay me
twice as many —
oh, precious henny-penny!'
Alas, her greed was such
she gave it far too much
till, over-loaded,
the fed-up hen
exploded.

Moral:
Be content with what you've got;
Push your luck — you'll lose the lot.

Ian Serraillier